A Note to Parents

DK READERS is a compelling program for beginning readers, designed in conjunction with leading literacy experts, including Dr. Linda Gambrell, Professor of Education at Clemson University. Dr. Gambrell has served as President of the National Reading Conference and the College Reading Association, and the International Reading Association.

Beautiful illustrations and superb full-color photographs combine with engaging, easy-to-read stories to offer a fresh approach to each subject in the series. Each DK READER is guaranteed to capture a child's interest while developing his or her reading skills, general knowledge, and love of reading.

The five levels of DK READERS are aimed at different reading abilities, enabling you to choose the books that are exactly right for your child:

Pre-level 1: Learning to read
Level 1: Beginning to read
Level 2: Beginning to read alone
Level 3: Reading alone
Level 4: Proficient readers

The "normal" age at which a child begins to read can be anywhere from three to eight years old. Adult participation through the lower levels is very helpful for providing encouragement, discussing storylines, and sounding out unfamiliar words.

No matter which level you select, you can be sure that you are helping your child learn to read, then read to learn!

LONDON, NEW YORK, MUNICH,
MELBOURNE, AND DELHI

Author Michele R. Wells
Senior Editor Ros Walford
Senior Art Editor Ann Cannings
Senior DTP Designer David McDonald
Production Controller Sophie Argyris
Proofreader Cecile Landau
Associate Publisher Nigel Duffield

Reading Consultant
Deborah Lock

First American Edition, 2012

Published in the United States by DK Publishing
375 Hudson Street, New York, New York 10014

10 9 8 7 6 5 4 3 2 1
001–184665–Jun/12

Copyright © 2012 Dorling Kindersley Limited

Published in Great Britain by Dorling Kindersley Limited

DK books are available at special discounts when purchased in bulk
for sales promotions, premiums, fund-raising, or educational use.
For details, contact: DK Publishing Special Markets, 375 Hudson
Street, New York, New York 10014
SpecialSales@dk.com

A catalog record for this book is available
from the Library of Congress.

ISBN: 978-0-7566-9386-2

Color reproduction by Media Development & Printing Ltd., U.K.
Printed and bound in China by L. Rex Printing Co. Ltd.

The publisher would like to thank the following for their kind
permission to reproduce their photographs:
a=above, b=below/bottom, c=center, l=left, r=right, t=top

The publisher would like to thank the following for their kind
permission to reproduce their photographs:
(a-above; b-below/bottom; c-center; f-far; l-left; r-right; t-top)
Alamy: Jack Maguire (25); **Dorling Kindersley:** Alex Wilson, ©
Dorling Kindersley, courtesy of the Charlestown Shipwreck and
Heritage Centre, Cornwall (47tl); Peter Hayman © The British
Museum (23br). **Jacket: Alamy:** Jack Maguire (front cover).
All other images © Dorling Kindersley
For further information see: www.dkimages.com

For Nathan and Colby Bavaro

Discover more at
www.dk.com

Contents

DK READERS

READING
3
ALONE

Ghost Stories

Written by Michele R. Wells

DK Publishing

How to Tell a Good Ghost Story

It's getting late. The moon is out. It's time for a good scare with some ghost stories! Ghost stories are best when they make you shiver and shake. You can make them scarier if you tell them well.

Turn Out The Lights

There's nothing better for a ghost story than a dark night and a campfire. But there are other ways to create a spooky mood, too!

Get your friends to sit in a circle. Turn off all the lights. If grown-ups are around, ask them to light candles. Sit down and hold a flashlight so that just your face is lit.

Speak Softly

The best way to tell a ghost story is to speak softly. If you are quiet, your friends will have to listen hard to what you're saying. Speak slowly, too. This adds to the suspense and gives them time to wonder what will happen next.

Don't Explain Too Much

Have you ever watched a movie that was scary until the monster or ghost appeared on screen? Often, what's in your mind is much scarier than anything you see. Don't use too many details when telling your story. Use just enough for your friends to get the idea—but leave the rest to their imaginations.

Make It Sound Real

Most ghost stories are made up of all kinds of spooky sounding things that don't exist in real life. What makes them scary is thinking these things could have really happened. If a story begins "This happened to my cousin's friend last year," it will be much scarier to hear than one that starts out "Once upon a time."

So try to add to the story. Use places you know in your town. If you are camping, think about saying that the story happened in that very campsite. Use the woods or lake nearby. Put in people you know. Adding real people or places will make your story sound scarier.

Look Them In The Eye

Look at each of your friends as you tell your story. They'll feel like you are speaking to them. This is what a good storyteller does.

Make It Your Own

The stories in this book are just ideas. They are a place to start. You may have heard versions of them before, because ghost stories are often told and retold everywhere. These stories are not very detailed. As you read each one, you can think about how to change it to make it scarier for your friends. First, make each story your own. Then, make it as scary as you can.

The Half-Moon

William had spent the day at the carnival with his friends. It was getting dark, and some of the tents were starting to close. The friends finished their popcorn and cotton candy. They drank one last soda and started for the exit. William had promised his mother that he would come straight home that night.

Near the gate was a strange, silvery tent. It was still open. William looked at his watch. He knew that he had to leave, but there was something interesting about that tent. It had a black-and-red flag flying from the top and seemed to be lit by an eerie glow. William just had to check out this tent.

William said goodbye to his
friends and ducked inside. There,
at a low table draped with a purple
cloth, sat an old woman. She didn't
have a crystal ball or a set of cards.
She wasn't surrounded by candles
or strange carvings. She wasn't
wearing mystical rings or necklaces.
In fact, she looked a bit like
William's grandmother.

She said she was there to
tell his fortune. He sat down
on the chair in front of her.
"Tonight," she told him,
"the half-moon will last
for many days." He
waited for her to say more,
but that was all. William
stood up and thanked her.
He wasn't going to be late after
all, but that fortune sure was
a disappointment.

William decided to cut through
an open field to get home. When he
was halfway across it, the moon came
out from behind the clouds. It was
a half-moon, just as the woman had
said. What did she mean that it
would last for many days?

Just then, William tripped and stumbled forward. He had come across the top of an old well, half-buried in the long grass. He reached out to grab on to something—anything—and caught the edge of an old, metal lid as he tumbled down. He fell a long way.

William waited for his eyes to adjust to the darkness. He had landed on something hard. He reached into his pocket and pulled out his cell phone. It was smashed into pieces. Now he couldn't phone for help. There was nothing else down there with him—no ladder, no water or food. There was no way to get out, and he was all alone.

He looked up again. The rusty, metal lid was pulled halfway across the opening of the well. Moonlight was streaming through the other half. The far-away opening itself looked like a half-moon.

The old woman had said that it would last for many days.

William heard a low, growling sound. He turned to see the bright eyes and twitching snout of a huge, hungry creature. It was only a few feet away.

He wasn't alone after all.

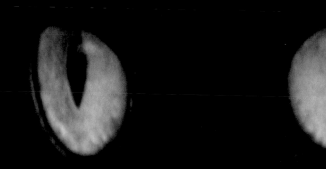

When the Clock Strikes Thirteen

Andrew was walking home after school one day, swinging his backpack. He had nothing special to do that afternoon, so he was not in much of a hurry. The sun was bright overhead, and there was a crisp fall breeze blowing.

He took a shortcut through an alley. The alley curved past the remains of a house that had recently burned down. There, he saw a boy about his age leaning up against the fence. The boy was tossing a baseball straight up in the air and catching it.

Andrew looked at the boy, and the boy looked back at Andrew. Andrew pulled his catcher's mitt from his backpack. Without a word, the boy picked up his bat and followed Andrew through the alley to the park on the other side.

They spent the day playing two-man baseball. Andrew had always been pretty good at batting and catching, but the boy, Jim, was just a little bit better. It was a great game. They played until the sun set, then played some more. One by one, the streetlights started turning on.

"I'd better get home," Andrew finally said to Jim. "Thanks for a great game." Jim shook his hand and told him he'd see Andrew around.

"Want to play again tomorrow?" Andrew asked. Jim shook his head and said, "I'll see you next when the clock strikes thirteen." With that he grabbed his stuff and ran back through the alley.

Andrew's mother was reading the newspaper when he walked in. She said that there had been a terrible fire the week before. The house that had burned down was only a few blocks away. "Was the boy who died in your class?" she asked Andrew. "He was exactly your age."

Andrew thought for a minute. "I haven't heard anything about it at school," he said. "What was the boy's name?"

His mother looked back through the newspaper article. "His name was Jim," she said. "He was on the baseball team."

Andrew never saw the boy again, but he also never forgot Jim's final words. He always made sure that he was fast asleep well before midnight. He didn't want to take the chance that Jim would keep his promise.

People say that on a dark night— just like this one—you can hear Jim running the bases and laughing. Listen closely. What was that?

The Hand

Mark and Emma were two seniors from the high school down the road. One Friday evening, they went to see a horror film. When the movie ended, Mark asked if Emma wanted to take a drive. They went out to the woods on the edge of town.

They parked in a darkened spot. It was so heavily wooded that even the moonlight didn't come through the

branches. Mark turned off the engine, but left the radio on. He was looking for a good station. A breaking news report came on. The newscaster said that a patient with a hook for a hand had escaped from the local asylum. The police advised everyone to stay home and lock their doors and windows. The patient was extremely dangerous.

Emma wanted to go home, but Mark laughed at her. "You're just scared because we saw that horror movie tonight," he said. "There's nothing to worry about."

Suddenly, they heard a loud bang. It came from somewhere near the back of the car. Mark turned the lights back on and looked through the rearview mirror. He couldn't see anything. "It's probably just a branch that fell," he told Emma.

Another bang, louder than before, came from the back of the car. This bang shook the car so hard that it bounced up and down. Mark took off his seatbelt to go investigate. "It's too dark out there," cried Emma. "You won't see anything. Let's get out of here."

They sat quietly for a moment, listening. Just then, a rough, metallic scraping sounded overhead, as if someone—or something—was on top of the car. The sound moved slowly from the back of the car toward the front. It stopped when it was directly above them.

Mark turned the key and threw the car into reverse. He backed out of the spot so quickly that the tires spun wildly on the leafy ground. He raced back to Emma's house, then jumped out of the car. He wanted to make sure there was no damage.

He was staring at a strange set of dents in his rear bumper when he heard a loud scream.

Mark ran around the car to find Emma crying. She pointed in horror at her door handle.

Hanging from it was a bloody hook.

The Girl on the Road

Last winter, my cousin, Alex, was driving on a winding highway road near his home. It had just started to snow. The road was getting icy, so he slowed down. He didn't want to miss his exit.

As he neared his turn, he slowed down even more. He thought he saw a girl on the side of the road. It was very cold out, and the girl was wearing just a long, white dress. She didn't have a coat or scarf. She was shivering. It was late and there were no other cars on the road. Alex pulled over near the girl. He opened the door and asked if she needed some help.

The girl walked slowly over to the open door. Her hair was very blonde, and her eyes were so light they were almost colorless. Her skin was pale. There were snowflakes on her eyelashes. When she spoke, he had to listen hard to hear her voice over the howling of the wind.

She said her name was Ellen. She had been on her way home from a dance. She had gotten into an argument with her date, and had jumped out of the car. She had been walking home when it started to snow. She had left her coat in the car and was freezing.

Alex offered to take her home. Ellen smiled gratefully and got into the car. She said very little—only giving directions, such as "Turn here" and "Go through the next light." He turned the car's heater on high, but she kept shivering.

Finally, they turned down a dark road. Ellen pointed to a house on the opposite side of the street. She said it was her parents' home. The lights were out and no one seemed to be waiting up.

He unlocked the door and turned to open it for Ellen, but she was gone. There was nothing in the passenger's seat but a few melted streaks of snow.

Alex peered out in the snow but saw no sign of Ellen. Worried, he got out of the car to look for her. He ran up to her parents' house. Even though it was late, he rang the doorbell.

An elderly woman answered the door. She was dressed in a robe, and looked sleepy. The doorbell had woken her. Alex apologized for disturbing her. He said he had brought her daughter home. He asked if she had come inside.

"Did you pick her up on the highway?" the old woman asked.

Alex nodded. "She told me that she was on her way home from a dance."

The old woman sighed and pulled her robe tighter. "That was Ellen. She was on her way home from a dance five years ago. She got into a fight with her date and tried to walk home. A car slid on the icy road and hit her. She was killed."

Alex turned to look again at his car. The door was open, and light was streaming out.

The old woman continued, "And every year since, on this night, she tries again to get home. Thank you for picking her up."

The Third Door on the Left

Jake and Jennifer were upset. They didn't get to go to camp this summer with the rest of their friends. Instead, they had to stay with their great-aunt, Rose, in her rickety, old house by the lake.

The house was huge—way too big for just their aunt—and she was too old to be much fun. She didn't even own a television, never mind a computer or any video games! The lake was too cold for swimming, Aunt Rose didn't have a boat, and there was no one else their age who lived nearby. It was going to be a long summer.

After dinner the first night, Aunt Rose showed them around. Most of the rooms were plain. She made a big show of opening the door of the library on the second floor. "You may read anything you like in here," she said, "and go into any of the other rooms on this floor. However, you are not allowed to go near the third door on the left." Jennifer rolled her eyes. The books were old and dusty. They wouldn't be interesting.

For a week, Jake and Jennifer explored every room in the old house, looking for games or puzzles, or anything else that might be fun. One night, they had nothing to do. Aunt Rose was fast asleep by the fireplace. "Let's try the library," suggested Jake. They walked around the room. Jennifer read the titles of the books. They were collections of ghost stories! Maybe they wouldn't be so bad after all.

Jake and Jennifer each grabbed a book. They sat down on the cobwebby, old chairs and tried reading aloud to each other. Some of the books had missing pages, so they couldn't find out how the stories ended.

Others were so ancient that they just fell apart in their hands.

"This is dumb," Jake said after a while. "There's nothing to do in this place. Let's just go to sleep."

"I'm not tired," Jennifer replied. "And there's still one room we haven't checked out…"

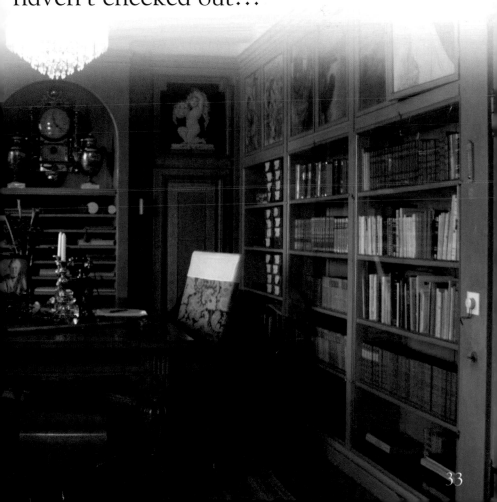

They jumped up and ran to the door. They looked carefully up and down the hall. Aunt Rose was nowhere to be seen.

Slowly, Jake and Jennifer crept down the hallway. They stood in front of the third door on the left. It looked no different from any of the other doors in the house.

Jake put his hand out and slowly turned the knob. It wasn't even locked! He smiled at Jennifer and pushed open the door...

Aunt Rose finished her eggs alone the next morning. She made a cup of tea and washed the dishes. Then, she shuffled up the stairs to the second floor.

There, in front of the open door, stood Jake and Jennifer. Jake still had his outstretched hand on the doorknob. They were both standing completely still. Their hair had turned stark white, and they had looks of terror on their faces.

Aunt Rose shook her head and slowly returned downstairs.

The Shadow in the Mirror (or, Bloody Mary)

Long ago, there were deep, dark woods in this town. And in the woods lived a woman. No one had seen her for many years, but they heard her terrible singing late at night when the moon was full. People called her "Bloody Mary." They said that she liked to drink blood.

Parents warned their children not to stay out late during the full moon. Boys and girls who missed curfew on those nights would go missing. One by one, they would disappear. Their families searched everywhere. The police would bring dogs to sniff out their trails. The clues always ended where the woods began.

One night a boy named John stayed at school to play basketball. He lost track of the time, and didn't leave until well after dark. He had to pass by the woods on the way home. Suddenly, he began to scream.

A man was passing by in a car. He heard the screams, but could not find John. He saw an eerie green light in the trees. The light was all around Bloody Mary. She was singing. As he watched, she seemed to grow younger. Then she disappeared. John was never heard from again.

That night, people in the town had enough. They set the woods on fire. People said they heard Mary singing at first, then screaming. They said she died in the fire. The trees all burned down, but her house was still there. Behind it was a pile of bones. The bones were from all the missing children.

Mary had chopped them up. She had been drinking their blood to stay young.

There was nothing left inside the house except a cracked mirror and a piece of paper. On the paper was a warning. It said that Mary would come back someday. And this is how to bring her back:

Wait until midnight. Shut off all the lights. Look in a mirror, and repeat her name three times. Say "Bloody Mary, Bloody Mary, Bloody Mary." If you see a shadow behind you in the mirror, it's Mary. And you'd better run. She will be after your blood!

Man's Best Friend

Ever since Tommy was a little boy, his dog, Spike, had been there for him. Spike was Tommy's best friend. Whenever Tommy got scared or felt alone, Spike would curl up under his bed. Tommy would stretch his hand down and Spike would lick his fingers. Tommy was comforted, knowing that Spike was there. He would fall asleep smiling, glad that his dog was nearby.

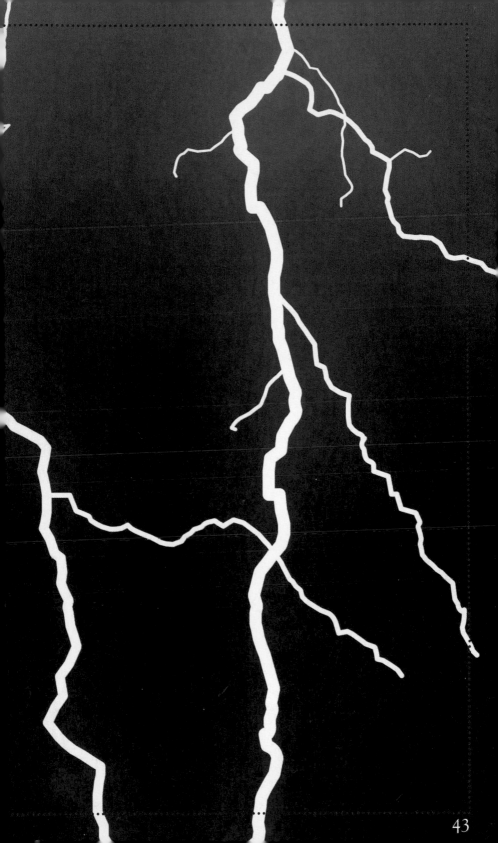

Now Tommy is
13 years old. He is too
old to get frightened by noises
during the night, and he doesn't feel
alone much anymore. However, on
this night a terrible thunderstorm was
raging outside. His parents were at
a wedding and wouldn't be home
until early morning. Tommy crawled
into bed but could not sleep. He

heard a soft whimper from under the bed. Tommy stretched his hand down. His dog began to lick his hand softly.

Tommy tossed and turned. He put the pillow over his head. He tried to fall asleep, despite the crashing thunder and crackling lightning. Finally, Tommy stretched his hand down beside the bed again. The dog's continued, soft licking and whimpering made him feel better. At last, he fell fast asleep.

His parents finally came home around three in the morning. They opened his bedroom door. Light streamed into his room. Groggily, Tommy sat up, wondering what was wrong. His parents never woke him up in the middle of the night.

"What do you mean by leaving the dog outside in the rain all night?" his father demanded.

Tommy started to protest, "Spike isn't outside. He's under my—"

Just then, the dog bounded into Tommy's room, soaked to the bone. He shook his body and the cold rain sprayed off his fur. He settled under Tommy's bed and began licking his hand.

Find Out More
Books

Creepy Campfire Tales
By James D. Adams
A collection of original, scary stories to
tell around the campfire. For ages 9 and up.

Scary Stories to Tell in the Dark
By Alvin Schwartz
Spine-tingling, classic tales of horror.
For ages 9 and up.

Ask the Bones
By Arielle North Olson and Howard Schwartz
This collection of scary folktales features stories
from many different cultures. For ages 8 and up.

Ghost Hunt: Chilling Tales of the Unknown
By Jason Hawes, Grant Wilson, and Cameron Dokey
This collection of scary stories is based on case files
from the Atlanta Paranormal Society, TAPS.
For ages 9 and up.

**Beware!: R. L. Stine Picks His Favorite
Scary Stories**
By R. L. Stine
Bestselling horror author R. L. Stine compiles stories
from Ray Bradbury, Bram Stoker, Edward Gorey, and
more in this read-aloud collection. For ages 8 and up.

Glossary

Ancient
Very old

Appear
To be or come
into sight

Asylum
A hospital or other
place where the sick
or mentally ill are
cared for

Cobwebby
Covered with cobwebs
or spider webs

Colorless
Without color; pale

Crept
Walked slowly
and quietly

Eerie
Strange and
frightening; creepy

Exist
To be found in
real life

Fortune
Chance or luck;
sometimes used to
mean future events

Groggily
Tiredly

Investigate
To look closely; to
discover the facts
of an event

Midnight
Twelve o'clock in
the morning; the time
when night officially
becomes day

Mood
An overall feeling

Mystical
Strange and
mysterious

Rickety
Old and unsteady;
likely to fall apart

Shuffled
Slowly sliding one's
feet along the ground
while walking

Suspense
A feeling of worry
or nervousness
about what will
happen next

Whimper
A low, whining sound